BORN IS THE KING

IT'S CHRISTMAS!

A Multi-Generational Christmas Celebration
for Adult Choir, Student Choir, Children's Choir and Orchestra!

Created by Luke Gambill and Sue C. Smith

Available Products:

Choral Book	45757-2404-7
CD Preview Pak	45757-2404-1
Listening CD	45757-2404-2
Split-Track Accompaniment CD	45757-2404-3
Audio Stem Files	45757-2404-4
Split-Track Accompaniment DVD (Disc 2 contains .mov Files)	45757-2404-6
Orchestration/Conductor's Score CD-Rom	45757-2404-8
Soprano Rehearsal Track CD	45757-2405-0
Alto Rehearsal Track CD	45757-2405-5
Tenor Rehearsal Track CD	45757-2405-6
Bass Rehearsal Track CD	45757-2405-7
Drums Rehearsal Track (Drums-Left, Full Mix-Right)	45757-2405-1
Bass Guitar Rehearsal Track (Bass Guitar-Left, Full Mix-Right)	45757-2405-2
Guitar Rehearsal Track (Acoustic-Left, Electric-Right)	45757-2405-3
Piano/Keyboard Rehearsal Track (Piano-Left, Full Mix-Right)	45757-2405-4

Instrumentation:

Flute 1, 2
Oboe
Clarinet 1, 2
F Horn 1, 2 (Alto Sax)
Trumpet 1
Trumpet 2, 3
Trombone 1, 2 (Tenor Sax/Baritone T.C.)
Trombone 3
Tuba
Percussion 1
Percussion 2
Timpani
Harp
Violin 1
Violin 2
Viola
Cello
String Bass (Bassoon)
Synth String Reduction
Rhythm
Drum Set

a division of

www.brentwoodbenson.com

CONTENTS

Born Is the King (It's Christmas)

Words and Music by
MATT CROCKER
and SCOTT LIGERTWOOD
Arranged by Luke Gambill

10

12

14

89

Do-doot do-doot doot do   do.   Do-doot do-doot doot do do do.

Ah____

Born is   the King, re - joice in the day.____   It's Christ - mas!

D♭

91

Do-doot do-doot doot do   do.   Do-doot do-doot doot do   do.

Ah____

Make   a___ joy - ful   sound.____   It's Christ - mas!

A♭

Do-doot do-doot doot do do. Do-doot do-doot doot do do do. Ah____

Do-doot do-doot doot do do. Do-doot do-doot doot do do do. Ah____

Do-doot do-doot doot do do. Do-doot do-doot doot do do. Ah____

Do-doot do-doot doot do do. Do-doot do-doot doot do do. Ah____

Christmas Day

Words and Music by
MICHAEL W. SMITH, WES KING
and CINDY MORGAN
Arranged by Bradley Knight

NARRATOR 1: This is the story of Jesus and how He came to earth — the story of what Christmas is all about.

NARRATOR 2: Our celebrations are aglow with candles and strings of lights, and they're accompanied by familiar carols and songs of the season.

NARRATOR 1: We mark the days and weeks leading up to December 25th with baking and shopping, hiding presents and going to parties. We observe the eve of our Savior's birth with church services and re-telling what we know of that night in Bethlehem.

(Music starts)

NARRATOR 2: And we awaken on Christmas morning to family gatherings and gift-giving. Every tradition is another way for us to say, "Jesus has come and that news fills us with joy!"

14

LADIES
mp

("Cot-nnn," no hard "t")

You see that old___ tree down cot - ton lane.___

day.

D♭   A♭/C   G♭2/B♭   D♭/A♭

16

Those lights keep shin - ing; it's al - ways the same.

Al - ways the same.

G♭2   D♭2/F   D♭/F   E♭m9   A♭7sus   A♭7

18

We hear the church bells ring out to say,___

D♭   A♭6/C   A♭/C   Fsus   F7/A   B♭m   B♭m/A♭

28

Swing the lights and hang the stock-ings,   de-co-rate with green and red,

day."

made the cook-ies for ol' San - ta,   made a run-way for   his sled.

30

41
Joy to the world! For ev - 'ry na - tion, for
(Don't overpower kids.)
Joy to the world!
T.
Bb/D F/C Bb F/A
43
ev - 'ry boy and girl. Let's light a can - dle;
Let's light a can - dle;
Gm7 Bb Bb(#4)/C Bb/D C/E C F C6/E C/E
3
3

Come

Words and Music by
LEE BLACK, GINA BOE
and CLIFF DUREN
Arranged by Cliff Duren

NARRATOR 2:   We see Christmas through each verse of Scripture that tells us what happened so long ago.

(Music starts)

NARRATOR 1:   But what if we saw it through a different lens — through the eyes of those who had been promised that a Messiah would appear — those who had spent a lifetime watching and waiting and longing for that promise to be fulfilled.

40

41

42

44

46

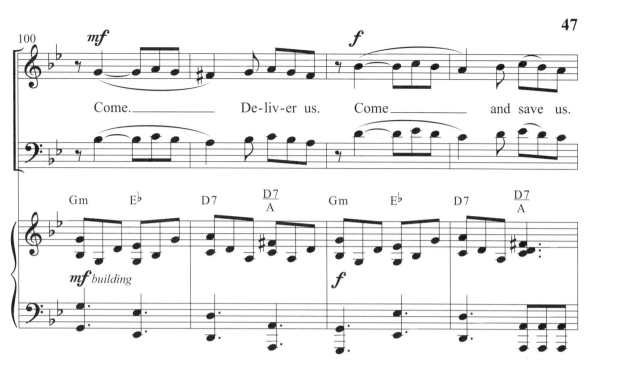

Come._____ De-liv-er us. Come_____ and save us.

Come,___ O come, Lord, come!_____

When Hope Came Down

Words and Music by
BEN GLOVER and KARI JOBE
Arranged by Luke Gambill

NARRATOR 1: Every prophecy made about the Savior's coming was about to converge in a little town not far from Jerusalem.

(Music starts)

NARRATOR 2: God would use a virgin girl and a poor carpenter, a Roman ruler and a Bethlehem innkeeper, some ordinary shepherds and a host of angels.

NARRATOR 1: And God would send His only begotten Son to a world that desperately needed Him.

le - hem. All of the an - gels lift - ed up their voic - es and

filled the night with hal - le - lu - jahs! God __ is with us now.

__ Ev - 'ry-one, come and join the heav'n - ly cho - rus. Our

Sav - ior King is here__ be - fore us! Oh,__ to hear__ the sound,

__ the song__ cre - a - tion sang when Hope came down.

So this was tru-ly

God wrapped up in a tat - tered blan - ket.

Hope was fi - n'lly here, sleep-ing while the

world a - wak - ened.___ And re - demp - tion be - gan

with a Ba - by___ in Beth -

54

Sav - ior King is here __ be - fore us! Oh, __ to hear __ the sound,

the song __ cre - a - tion sang when Hope came down.

So, let us sing

SOLO

When Hope came down. All of the

an - gels lift - ed up their voic - es and filled the night with hal-

- le - lu - jahs! God is with us now. Ev-'ry-one,

When Hope came down.

When Hope came, when Hope came down.

SOLO
mf

GUYS mf

C2

When___ Hope

SOPRANOS
mf When Hope came down.___

ALTOS
When Hope came down.

G2

60

A Humble Bed

Words and Music by
LUKE GAMBILL and JOEL LINDSEY
Arranged by BJ Davis and Luke Gambill

NARRATOR 2: Luke 2 says Mary brought forth her firstborn Son, and wrapped Him in swaddling cloths, and laid Him in a manger because there was no room for them in the inn.

(Music starts)

NARRATOR 1: Now, we have imagined that innkeeper in countless ways, from cold to clueless to concerned. Whoever he was, whatever he did or said, Jesus was born just the way God had intended all along.

searched all o - ver town, but there was no room to be found. The

night was here, they had no place to stay. The

inn was full,_ and yet I could - n't turn them a -

way._____ It was - n't

64

leav-ing gold-en streets be-hind, but He

did-n't seem to mind, and He was here. I did-n't know it then,

who would ev-er think this ti-ny Ba - by

could be Him.＿＿ It was-n't

much, no king-ly throne, a hum-ble

bed in from the cold. For I'm just a

64

have no wealth to give. It was just a cat-tle stall, a bed of straw, where no

Ah

Ooo

Am D/F# G C2 G/B

66

47

mp

child should have to live. But He need-ed

Ah

Am D#°7 Em

Glorious Jesus

Words and Music by
MICHAEL FORDINAL and BRIAN HITT
Arranged by Daniel Semsen

NARRATOR 2:   They were ordinary men, doing their ordinary jobs out on the Bethlehem hills that night.

(Music starts)

NARRATOR 1:   But one moment of blinding light from above, a messenger from heaven, a sky set ablaze with glory — one moment would change their lives forever.

81

82

84

Do You Hear What I Hear?

Words and Music by
NOEL REGNEY and GLORIA SHAYNE
Arranged by Landy Gardner, Joy Gardner
and Christopher Phillips

(Music starts)

NARRATOR 1: A new light pierced the darkness of that holy night, and far from Bethlehem, there were men who took notice.

NARRATOR 2: To these wealthy scholars, the star announced the birth of a ruler, a leader… perhaps a King. It declared the coming of someone who would change the world.

NARRATOR 1: It's what the star has always said. Jesus has come and nothing will ever be the same.

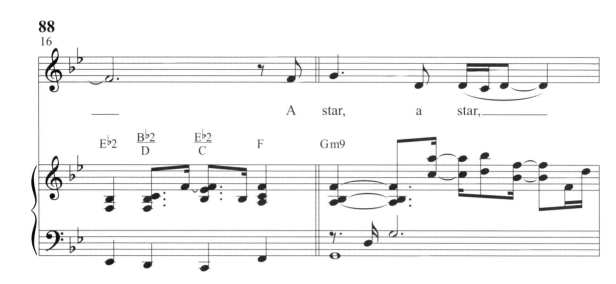

30

Ring-ing through the sky, shep-herd boy,

32

62

do you hear what I hear? Oh, a

Do you hear what I hear?

song, a song____ high a-bove the trees, with a

CHOIR

Ooo____ Ooo

voice as____ big as____ the sea,____ with____ a____

Ooo____

102

I Heard the Bells on Christmas Day

Words by
HENRY WADSWORTH LONGFELLOW

Additional Words and Music by
MARK HALL, DALE OLIVER
and BERNIE HERMS
Arranged by Cliff Duren

NARRATOR 2:   Before Jesus was born, God's Word says the people "walked in darkness." But then He came, and Scripture says He was the "light of the world." *(Music starts)* Yet in many ways, we still live in a world shrouded in night.

NARRATOR 1:   Those who don't know Jesus cry out for hope and search for peace. Those of us who do know Him and who follow Him, long for the day when His peace will reign, the day when He will come again.

110

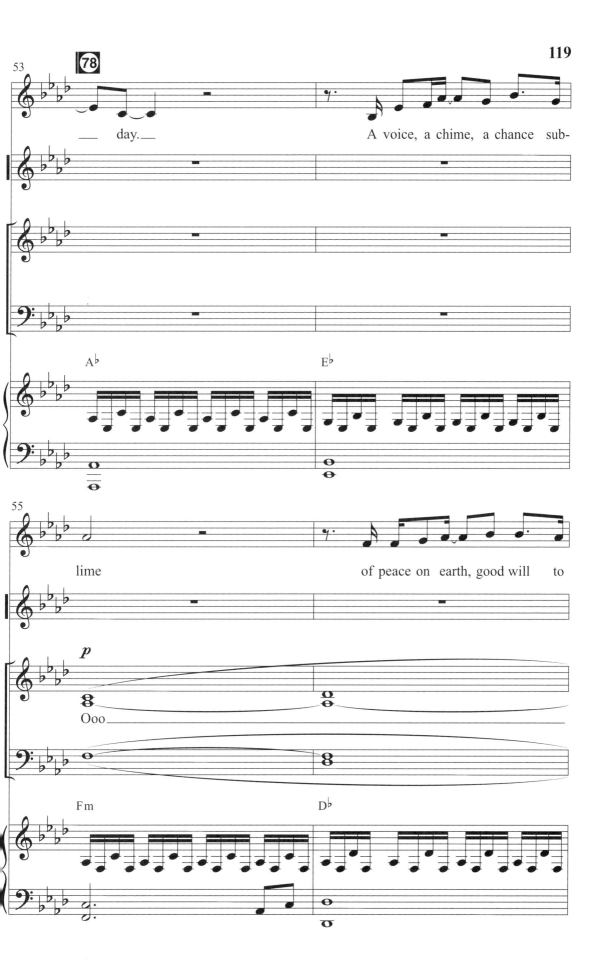

120

121

NARRATOR 2:   Luke 2:17-19 says, "After seeing him, the shepherds told everyone what had happened and what the angel had said to them about this child. All who heard the shepherd's story were astonished, but Mary kept all these things in her heart and thought about them often."

NARRATOR 1:   Just like the shepherds, we can't keep quiet about what happened in Bethlehem so long ago. We have to tell others that God sees us and He loves us. He loves us so much that He was willing to give His only Son Jesus to save us.

NARRATOR 2:   At the same time, like Mary we keep all these things in our hearts and ponder how amazing it is that God sees us and He loves us. He loves us so much that He was willing to give His only Son Jesus to save us.

(Music starts)

NARRATOR 1:   The bells of Christmas are ringing out the good news, "Unto you is born this day a Savior, who is Christ the Lord!" This is the reason we are filled with joy and hope.

NARRATOR 2:   So let's share the message with anyone who will listen, and let's live in a way that says His love makes all the difference.

NARRATOR 1:   The Lord has come!

NARRATOR 2:   Our King is born!

NARRATOR 1 & 2: It's Christmas!

Joy to the World

Traditional Words:
ISAAC WATTS

Traditional Music:
GEORGE FREDERICK HANDEL
New Words and Music by
CHRIS LOCKWOOD and JASON BARTON
Arranged by Luke Gambill

128

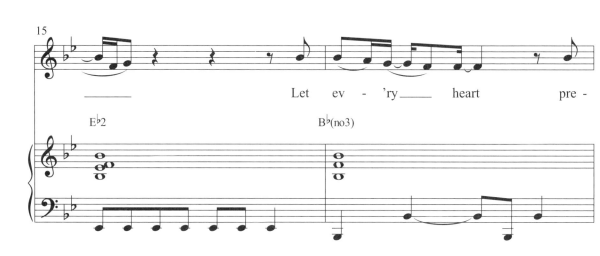

130

132

sing loud, joy to the world!

sing loud, joy to the world!

sing loud, joy to the world!

78

_ up your voice and make a joy - ful sound.__ Come on_

_ up your voice and make a joy - ful sound.__ Come on_

_ up your voice and make a joy - ful sound.__ Come on_

D9

79 **91**

_ sing__ loud, joy__ to the world! Ev -

_ sing__ loud, joy__ to the world! Ev -

unis.

_ sing__ loud, joy__ to the world! Ev -

unis.

F2   Bb2   C   Bb2   F/A   Fsus/G   F(no3)

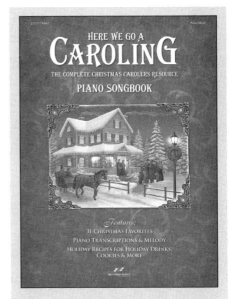
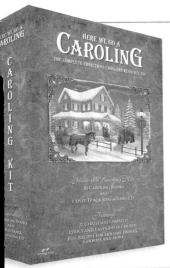

A Great Warm-Up Resource for Music Directors, Choir Members and Soloists!

Director's Edition

Singer's Edition

BRENTWOOD-BENSON®
music publishing

Vocal Ease is a series of 13 exercises compiled by Dave Williamson as a result of scanning the globe for over 30 years in an effort to identify a warm-up sequence that <u>really</u> works. The exercises in this collection are the best of the best at actually preparing the voice for singing.

The exercises fall into 5 categories:

- **Breathing Exercises** - Proper breathing is the foundation of all singing. These exercises teach breathing technique, muscle development and breath control.

- **Cobweb Sweeping Exercises** - Helps attack and remove the undesirable things that have come to roost in the mouth and throat.

- **"First Song" Exercises** - Establishes the sound in the sinus cavity; helps with the development of unification of pronunciation, accuracy of pitch - both hearing and singing, and connecting of the melodic line.

- **Tongue and Lip Exercises** - Focuses on getting sound in the sinus region. Limbering up exercise for the lips.

- **Combination Exercises** - Puts all the exercises together.

These exercises are very versatile: They can be used either in the context of a choir rehearsal, or individually in a choir member's home or car. Wherever you use them, they'll work, and they'll work great! Dave makes it easy for you to teach your choir these warm-ups.

In the **Director's Edition,** each exercise is prefaced with Dave's explanation of its purpose and includes a demonstration by Dave with his choir of how it is to be performed. The **Singer's Edition** includes the exercises only, without the explanations of each exercise. If you're serious about improving the sound of your choir, this series is for you!

CALL **1-800-846-7664,** visit **www.brentwoodbenson.com** or order from your **local Christian retailer** today!